C00 17786894

EDINBURGH CITY LIBRARIES

C000153103

WITHDRAWN

POEMS ABOUT OUR WORLD
EARTH-WISE

CHOSEN BY WENDY COOLING

Illustrated by Rowan Barnes-Murphy

W
FRANKLIN WATTS
NEW YORK · LONDON · SYDNEY
E·C·L

EDINBURGH CITY LIBRARIES

AC

C0017786894

LY BM CL

PR £10.99 V ASC 9/3/01 821 LA2

21 MAR 2001

First published in 2000 by Franklin Watts
96, Leonard Street, London EC2A 4XD

Franklin Watts Australia
14 Mars Road, Lane Cove, NSW 2066

© Franklin Watts 2000

Editor: Sarah Snashall
Designer: Louise Thomas
Border artwork: Diana Mayo

A CIP catalogue record for this book
is available from the British Library.

ISBN 0 7496 3480 4

Dewey classification 821.008

Printed in Hong Kong/China

Acknowledgments

The editor and publishers gratefully acknowledge
permission to reproduce the following copyright material.

What is the Sun? by Wes Magee. Reprinted by
permission of the author. *Sunset*, by June Crebbin.
Permission granted by the author. © 1992 June Crebbin
(first published in *The Dinosaur's Dinner*, Viking). *Silver*
by Walter de la Mare from *The Complete Poems of Walter
de la Mare*, 1969. Reprinted by permission of the Literary
Trustees of Walter de la Mare, and the Society of Authors
as their representative. *The Night Will Never Stay*, by
Eleanor Farjeon, from *Silver, Sand and Snow* (Michael
Joseph). Reprinted by permission of the author, c/o David
Higham Associates, 5-8 Lower John Street, Golden Square,
London W1R 4HA. *Spring*, by E. E. Cummings. Reprinted
from *Complete Poems 1904-1962*, by E. E. Cummings,
edited by George J. Firmage, by permission of
W. W. Norton & Company. © 1991 by the Trustees for
the E. E. Cummings Trust and George James Firmage.
Facts About Air, by John Foster. © 1991 John Foster (first
published in *Science Poetry*, edited by Robert Hull,
Wayland). Included by permission of John Foster. *August*,
by John Updike. © 1965 John Updike. All rights reserved.
Reprinted from *A Child's Calendar* by permission of
Holiday House, Inc. *Fun, fun, fungi* by Robert Fisher.
Permission granted by the author. *Spell of the Earth*, by
Elizabeth Jennings. Reprinted by permission of the author,
c/o David Higham Associates, 5-8 Lower John Street,
Golden Square, London W1R 4HA. *Our Tree*, by David
Harmer. Permission granted by the author. *Dis Fighting*,
by Benjamin Zephaniah. Permission granted by the author.
Everything Changes, by Cicely Herbert. Permission
granted by the author. *Beyond My House*, by Moira
Andrew. First published in *Dear Future ... A Time Capsule
of Poems*, edited by David Orme, Hodder Children's
Books, 1997. Permission granted by the author.

Every effort has been made to trace copyright, but if any
omissions have been made please let us know in order that
we may put it right in the next edition.

CONTENTS

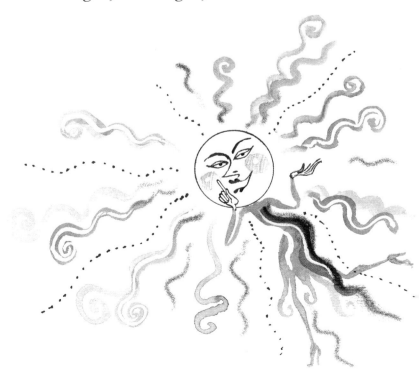

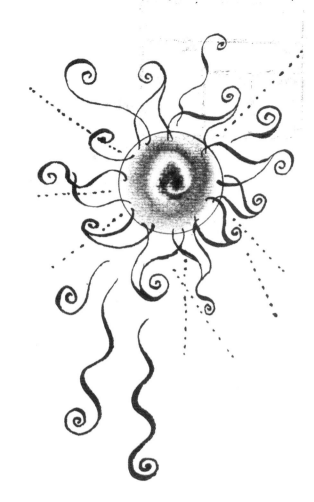

QUESTIONS AT NIGHT

Why
Is the sky?

What starts the thunder overhead?
Who makes the crashing noise?
Are the angels falling out of bed?
Are they breaking all their toys?

Why does the sun go down so soon?
Why do the night-clouds crawl
Hungrily up to the new-laid moon
And swallow it, shell and all?

If there's a Bear among the stars,
As all the people say,
Won't he jump over those pasture-bars
And drink up the Milky Way?

Does every star that happens to fall
Turn into a firefly?
Can't it ever get back to Heaven at all?
And why
Is the sky?

by Louis Untermeyer

MORNING

Will there really be a morning?
    Is there such a thing as day?
Could I see it from the mountains
    If I were as tall as they?
Has it feet like water lilies?
    Has it feathers like a bird?
Is it brought from famous countries
    Of which I've never heard?
Oh, some scholar! Oh, some sailor!
    Oh, some wise man from the skies!
Please to tell a little pilgrim
    Where the place called morning lies!

by Emily Dickinson

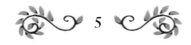

WHAT IS THE SUN?

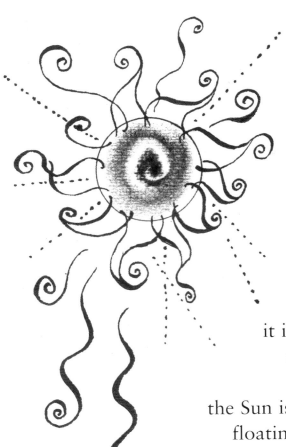

the Sun is an orange dinghy
    sailing across a calm sea

it is a gold coin
    dropped down a drain in Heaven

the Sun is a yellow beach ball
    kicked high into the summer sky

it is a red thumb-print
    on a sheet of pale blue paper

the Sun is a milk bottle's gold top
    floating in a puddle

by Wes Magee

HAVE YOU HEARD THE SUN SINGING?

Have you ever heard the sun in the sky
Man have you heard it?
Have you heard it break the black of night
Man have you heard it?
Have you heard it shouting its song, have you heard
It scorch up the air like a phoenix bird,
Have you heard the sun singing?

by John Smith

SUNSET

the sun
is having its last fling
of the day
tossing bright streamers
across the sky
ruffling the clouds
into ripples of pink
refusing to go in

until

promising to be back tomorrow
it slips behind the trees
beyond the sea of darkening fields.

by June Crebbin

THE MOON

The moon was but a chin of gold
A night or two ago,
And now she turns her perfect face
Upon the world below.

by Emily Dickinson

SILVER

Slowly, silently, now the moon
Walks the night in her silver shoon;
This way, and that, she peers, and sees
Silver fruit upon silver trees;
One by one the casements catch
Her beams beneath the silvery thatch;
Couched in his kennel, like a log,
With paws of silver sleeps the dog;
From their shadowy cote the white breasts peep
Of doves in a silver-feathered sleep;
A harvest mouse goes scampering by,
With silver claws, and silver eye;
And moveless fish in the water gleam,
By silver reeds in a silver stream.

by Walter de la Mare

THE FALLING STAR

I saw a star slide down the sky,
Blinding the north as it went by,
Too burning and too quick to hold,
Too lovely to be bought or sold,
Good only to make wishes on
And then forever to be gone.

by Sara Teasdale

STARLIGHT, STARBRIGHT

Starlight,
Starbright.
First star I see tonight,
I wish I may,
I wish I might,
Have this wish I wish tonight.

Traditional

THE NIGHT WILL NEVER STAY

The night will never stay,
The night will still go by,
Though with a million stars
You pin it to the sky;
Though you bind it with the blowing wind
And buckle it with the moon,
The night will slip away
Like sorrow or a tune.

by Eleanor Farjeon

11

SPRING

in Just-
spring   when the world is mud-
luscious the little
lame balloonman

whistles   far   and wee

and eddieandbill come
running from marbles and
piracies and it's
spring

when the world is puddle-wonderful

the queer
old balloonman whistles
far   and   wee
and bettyandisbel come dancing

from hop-scotch and jump-rope and

it's
spring
and
    the

       goat-footed

balloonMan   whistles
far
and
wee

by E. E. Cummings

NATURE

We have neither Summer nor Winter
Neither Autumn nor Spring.
We have instead the days
When the gold sun shines on the lush green canefields –
Magnificently.
The days when the rain beats like bullets on the roofs
And there is no sound but the swish of water in the gullies
And trees struggling in the high Jamaica winds.
Also there are the days when leaves fade from off guango trees
And the reaped canefields lie bare and fallow to the sun.
But best of all there are the days when the mango and the
    logwood blossom
When the bushes are full of the sound of bees and the scent of
    honey,
When the tall grass sways and shivers to the slightest breath of air,
When the buttercups have paved the earth with yellow stars
And beauty comes suddenly and the rains have gone.

by H. D. Carberry

FACTS ABOUT AIR

Scientists say
That air consists
Of about 78% nitrogen and 21% oxygen,
Plus some carbon dioxide
And small amounts
Of the rare gases – helium, argon and neon.

These are facts, I know.
But I also know
That when I go outside
On a spring morning
The air tastes as crisp
As a fresh lettuce
And that when I sit
On the patio
On a summer evening
The cool night air
Brushes my cheeks like a feather.

by John Foster

AUGUST

The sprinkler twirls.
  The summer wanes.
The pavement wears
  Popsicle stains.

The playground grass
  Is worn to dust.
The weary swings
  Creak, creak with rust.

The trees are bored
  With being green.
Some people leave
  The local scene

And go to seaside
  Bungalows
And take off nearly
  All their clothes.

by John Updike

SUMMER

Rushes in a watery place,
  And reeds in a hollow;
A soaring skylark in the sky,
  A darting swallow;
And where pale blossom used to hang
  Ripe fruit to follow.

by Christina Rossetti

15

FUN FUN FUNGI

Shhh! There is a secret in the woods
at autumn time
when leaves drip from the trees
and beads of dew hang like jewels
from spiders' webs
there is a secret in the woods
when cold winds
come whispering
fun fun fungi
from damp dark places
they rise and grow
toadstools
mushrooms
and fungi which cling and creep
along fallen logs
and in the hollows of
        trees
the fun fun fungi
of fairy rings

by Robert Fisher

AUTUMN

Evening sun – old man
Pushing barrow to a fire –
Smell of burning leaves.

by Neil Ferguson

WINTER WISE

Walk fast in snow, in frost walk slow,
And still as you go tread on your toe;
When frost and snow are both together,
Sit by the fire, and spare shoe leather.

Traditional

FOR, LO, THE WINTER IS PAST

For, lo, the winter is past
The rain is over and gone;
The flowers appear on the earth;
The time of the singing of birds is come
And the voice of the turtle is
heard in our land.

from The Song of Solomon, The Old Testament

THE ANSWERS

'When did the world begin and how?'
I asked a lamb,
   a goat,
     a cow.
'What is it all about and why?'
I asked a hog as he went by.
'Where will the whole thing end and when?'
I asked a duck,
   a goose,
     a hen:
And I copied all the answers too,
A quack
  a honk
    an oink
      a moo.

by Robert Clairmont

SPELL OF THE EARTH

I am the round of the globe,
The seas are my green robe,
I am where all plants grow
    And the trees know

From me they draw their strength,
From me all stems find length.
I am rich in countless ways,
    All footsteps give me praise.

by Elizabeth Jennings

IF THE EARTH

If the Earth
were only a few feet in diameter,
floating a few feet above a field somewhere,
people would come from everywhere to marvel
at it. People would walk around it, marvelling at its
big pools of water, its little pools and the water flowing
between the pools. People would marvel at the bumps on
it, and the holes in it, and they would marvel at the very thin
layer of gas surrounding it and the water suspended in the gas.
The people would marvel at all the creatures walking around
the surface of the ball, and at the creatures in the water. The
people would declare it as sacred because it was the only one,
and they would protect it so that it would not be hurt. The
ball would be the greatest wonder known, and people would
come to pray to it, to be healed, to gain knowledge, to know
beauty and to wonder how it could be. People would
love it, and defend it with their lives because they
would somehow know that their lives, their own
roundness, could be nothing without it. If
the Earth were only a few feet in
diameter.

by Steve Smith

YORUBA POEM

Enjoy the earth gently
Enjoy the earth gently
For if the earth is spoiled
It cannot be repaired
Enjoy the earth gently

Anon

In 1854 the President of the United States made an offer to buy some of the land occupied by the Indians. This is part of a letter attributed to Chief Seattle in reply to the President's offer.

CONDITION OF SALE

If we sell you land,
you must remember that it is sacred
and you must teach your children
that it is sacred.
The rivers
are our brothers,
they quench our thirst.
The rivers
carry our canoes
and feed our children.
If we sell you our land,
you must remember
that rivers are our brothers,
and yours,
and you must give the rivers the kindness
you would give
to any brother.

We know the white man does not
        understand our ways.
One portion of the land
is the same to him
as the next,
for he is a stranger
who comes in the night
and takes from the land whatever he needs.
The earth
is not his brother
but his enemy,
and when he has conquered it,
he moves on. His appetite
will devour the earth
and leave behind only
a desert.

I do not know.
Our ways are different
from your ways.
The sight of your cities
pains the eyes of the red man.
There is no
quiet place
in the white man's cities,
no place to hear
the unfurling
of the leaves in spring
or the rustle
of an insect's wings.
The air
is precious to the red man,
for all things share the same breath.
The white man
does not seem to notice the air he
        breathes…
But if we sell you
our land,
you must remember
that the air is precious to us,
that the air
shares its spirit
with all the life it supports.

So we will consider your offer
to buy our land,
but I will make one condition.
The white man must treat the land,
and the beasts of the land,
as his brothers.

by Chief Seattle

22

ONLY WHEN

Only when the last tree has died
and the last river has been poisoned
and the last fish has been caught
will we realize that we cannot eat money.

19th-Century Cree Indian

I THINK THAT I SHALL NEVER SEE

I think that I shall never see
A poem as lovely as a tree,
Poems are made by fools like me
But only God can make a tree.

by Alfred (Joyce) Kilmer

24

OUR TREE

It takes so long for a tree to grow
So many years of pushing the sky.

Long branches stretch their arms
Reach out with their wooden fingers.

Years drift by, fall like leaves
From green to yellow then back to green.

Since my Grandad was a boy
And then before his father's father

There's been an elm outside our school
Its shadow long across our playground.

Today three men ripped it down.
Chopped it up. It took ten minutes.

by David Harmer

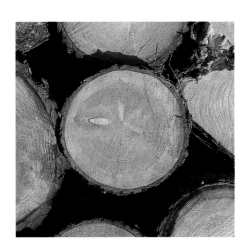

FELLING TREES

Stop! I cried to them,
     But the noise of their saws
Cut out my final plea.
     Everything is dying;
Dark sky where the flats will be.

by Adrian Youd (aged 13)

'MUMMY, OH MUMMY'

'Mummy, Oh Mummy, what's this pollution
That everyone's talking about?'
'Pollution's the mess that the country is in,
That we'd all be far better without.
It's factories belching their fumes in the air,
And the beaches all covered with tar,
Now throw all those sweet papers into the bushes
Before we get back in the car.'

'Mummy, Oh Mummy, who makes pollution,
And why don't they stop if it's bad?'
''Cos people like that just don't think about others,
They don't think at all, I might add.
They spray all the crops and they poison the flowers,
And wipe out the birds and the bees,
Now there's a good place we could dump that old mattress
Right out of sight in the trees.'

'Mummy, Oh Mummy, what's going to happen
If all the pollution goes on?'
'Well the world will end up like a second-hand junk-yard,
With all of its treasures quite gone.
The fields will be littered with plastics and tins,
The streams will be covered with foam,
Now throw those two pop bottles over the hedge,
Save us from carting them home.'

'But Mummy, Oh Mummy, if I throw the bottles,
Won't that be polluting the wood?'
'Nonsense! that isn't the same thing at all,
You just shut up and be good.
If you're going to start getting silly ideas
I'm taking you home right away,
'Cos pollution is something that other folk do,
We're just enjoying our day.'

Anon

DIS FIGHTING

No more fighting please, why can't we stop dis fighting,
dis fighting hurting me, why don't we start uniting,
dem fighting in Angola, dem fighting in Manchester,
dem fighting in Jamaica, and dem fighting in Leicester,
well i might be black, my people were once slaves,
but time goes on, and love comes in,
so now we must behave,
it could be that you're white, and i live in your land,
no reason to make war, dis hard fe understand,
skinheads stop dis fighting,
rude boys stop dis fighting,
dreadlocks stop dis fighting,
we must start uniting,
our children should be happy and they should live as one,
we have to live together so let a love grow strong,
let us think about each other, there's no need to compete,
if two loves love each other then one love is complete,
no more fighting please, we have to stop dis fighting,
dis fighting hurting me, time fe start uniting,
dis fighting have no meaning, dis fighting is not fair,
dis fighting makes a profit for people who don't care,
no more fighting please, we have to stop dis fighting,
dis fighting hurting me, the heathen love dis fighting.

by Benjamin Zephaniah

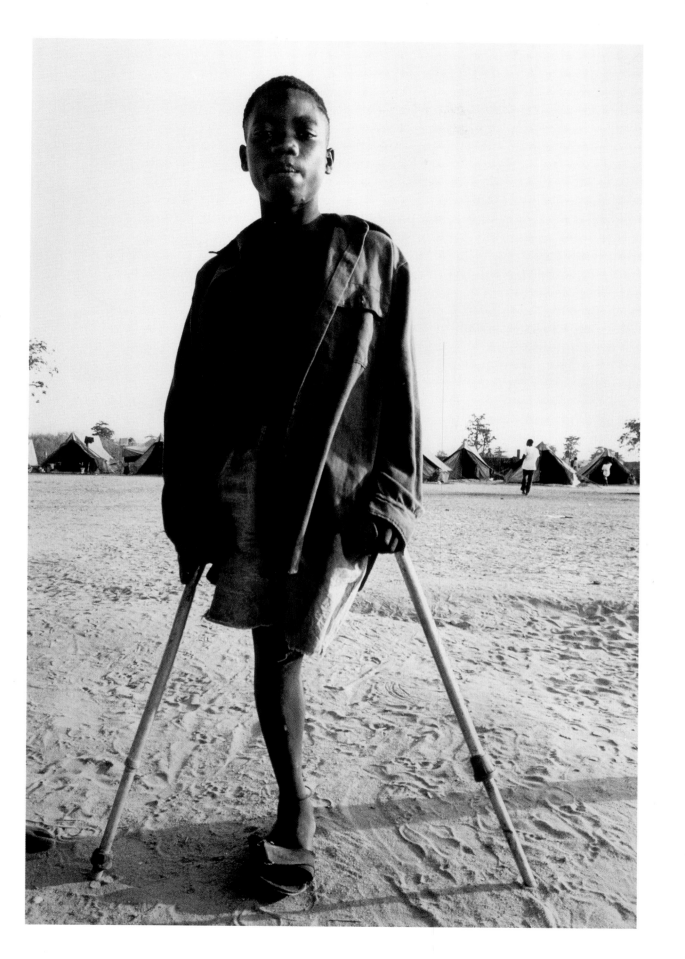

EVERYTHING CHANGES

(after Brecht)

Everything changes.
　　　　We plant
Trees for those born later –
but what's happened has happened
and poisons poured into the seas
cannot be drained out again.

What's happened has happened.
Poisons poured into the seas
cannot be drained out again
　　　　　But
Everything changes. We plant
trees for those born later.

by Cicely Herbert

BEYOND MY HOUSE

Above my house
is the blue of the sky,
fragile fishbone clouds
and the wind whispering
      like an untold wish.

Below my house
is the dark secret earth,
deep-spiralling roots
and the mystery of lives
      lived underground.

Around my house
is the garden wall, where
slow snails crawl and spiders
hang their webs, beaded
      like door curtains.

Beside my house
is an apple tree, a
shady place to hide
in summer, in winter
      a bony skeleton.

Over my house
is a rainbow, a magic
paint-splashed bridge
where raindrops shine
      like crystal beads.

Inside my house
is my family, my laughing,
crying, quarrelling family,
a place where I belong
      every single day.

Beyond my house
is the future, full of promise
as an unopened parcel
wrapped in fancy paper
      and silver ribbons.

by Moira Andrew

INDEX OF FIRST LINES

Picture credits

Cover image and title page:
Getty Images (Art Wolfe)

Inside images:
Eye Ubiquitous p.7 (Graham Wheatley)
Franklin Watts pp. 16t, 25
Images Colour Library p.15
Peter Newark's Western Americana p.23
(Edward S. Curtis)
PhotoDisc pp.8, 11, 19
Robert Harding p.5 (James Strachan)
Telegraph pp. 13 (Pascall
Dellazuana/GLMR), 24 (Planet
Earth/Eastcott and Momatiuk)
Tony Stone pp. 16b (Laurie Campbell),
21 (Eddie Soloway), 29 (James F
Housel), 30 (Jeremy Walker)